THE FIRST ADVENTURE

PILOT & HUXLEY

DAN McGUINESS

SCHOLASTIC INC.

NEW YORK TORONTO LONDON AUC
SYDNEY MEXICO CITY NEW DELHI HONG KONG

TO MY LOVING PARENTS, ELAINE AND BILL McGUINESS

FIRST PUBLISHED BY OMNIBUS BOOKS, A DIVISION OF SCHOLASTIC
AUSTRALIA PTY LIMITED, IN 2009.

THIS EDITION PUBLISHED UNDER LICENSE FROM SCHOLASTIC AUSTRALIA PTY LIMITED.

ISBN 978-0-545-38309-7

12 11 10 9 8 7 6 5 4 3 2 1   11 12 13 14 15 16/0

PRINTED IN THE U.S.A.   40

THIS EDITION FIRST PRINTING, SEPTEMBER 2011

DESIGN BY DAN McGUINESS AND CLARE OAKES
COVER DESIGN BY PHIL FALCO

WHOA! WHAT'S GOING ON?

DUDE! THAT'S YOU!

I THINK IT'S BROKEN, LIKE THE LEADER SAID.

POOF!

O-OKAY.

END OF CHAPTER ONE

EXCELLENT. SO YOU SENT THE TWO BOYS TO THE DIMENSION OF WIZZPOODOS. NOW, JUST HAND OVER THE GAME AND ALL THE MOVIE RENTALS YOU WANT ARE FREE.

GAME? YOUR SUBORDINATE JUST SAID TO GET RID OF THEM.

SO THEY STILL HAVE THE GAME, AND NOW THEY ARE IN ANOTHER DIMENSION?

WHO HIRED THE REAPER?

I DID, O GREAT MASTER.

HAVE A TASTE OF MY SNOT GUN.

BAROOB!

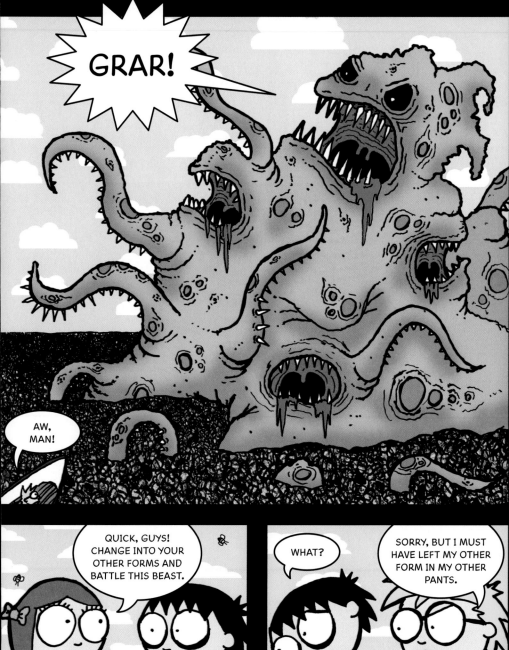

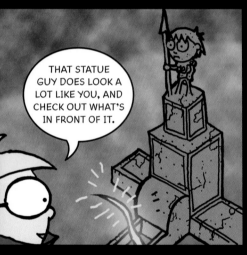

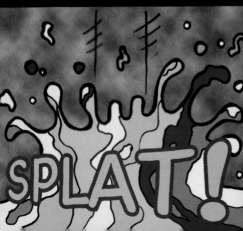

THAT'S A PROJECTION GUN. IT CAN TRANSFER INFORMATION DIRECTLY INTO SOMEONE'S MIND, LIKE A TEXT MESSAGE OR E-MAIL.

REALLY? LEADER! QUICK!! PLUG YOURSELF INTO THE PROJECTION GUN.

WHAT? WHY?

NO TIME TO EXPLAIN. JUST DO IT!

NOW SEND INTERNET INFORMATION INTO THE VORCONS' HEADS!

OKAY, WHAT DO YOU WANT ME TO SEND?

CLICK!

EVERYTHING! THE WHOLE UWW!

OKAY. READY, AIM, FIRE!

* "TO CHUCK A FRUITY" MEANS "TO THROW A FIT," WHICH HUXLEY DOES A LOT!

AFTERWORD

LOOK OUT FOR PILOT & HUXLEY IN THEIR NEXT ADVENTURE!

ABOUT THE AUTHOR

DAN McGUINESS WAS DISCOVERED AS AN INFANT AMONG THE SMOLDERING REMAINS OF A TOP SECRET LABORATORY.

HE GREW UP UNDER CLOSE SCRUTINY IN A MILITARY FACILITY OF UNCERTAIN LOCATION.

THE ARMY'S TOP SCIENTISTS ATTEMPTED TO HARNESS HIS EXTRAORDINARY POWERS OF STIR-FRY COOKERY AND REACHING THINGS ON HIGH SHELVES.

WHEN NOT HOOKED UP TO ELECTRODES, HE CAN BE FOUND IN HIS QUARTERS, MANICALLY SCRIBBLING COMICS ONTO LOLLIPOP WRAPPERS, SCRAPS OF TOILET PAPER, OR WHATEVER HE CAN GET HIS HANDS ON.

THOSE PAGES ARE COMPILED HERE AS HIS FIRST PUBLISHED BOOK, *PILOT & HUXLEY.*